THE HEYDAY OF THE TRACTION ENGINE

ERIC SAWFORD

IAN ALLAN
Publishing

Introduction

First published 1995

ISBN 0 7110 2362 X

Published by Ian Allan Publishing

an imprint of Ian Allan Ltd, Terminal House, Station Approach, Shepperton, Surrey TW17 8AS.

Printed by Ian Allan Printing Ltd, Coombelands House, Coombelands Lane, Addlestone, Weybridge, Surrey KT15 1HY.

Title page:
This broadside picture of a Fowler 10nhp 'Super Lion' crane engine, Works No 17106 *Duke of York* built in 1928, shows the engine without the crane jib fitted. Note the large gearing which works with the crane.

Most of this powerful engine's working life was spent with Marstons Road Services, Liverpool, where it acquired the well-deserved nickname *The Big Engine*. The engine has hauled many large, often outsized, loads around the country, including transformers, dynamos and even the rudder of HMS *Ark Royal* — a load of 80 tons — from Darlington to Birkenhead. One of the outsize loads handled by the engine was a 100ft x 11ft diameter fractioning tower, weighing 66 tons, from Sheffield to Liverpool.

Moving heavy loads of this type required exceptional skills by the crew and careful planning of the route.

Steam power was once a very common sight working on the farms and highways of the British Isles. Over the years it had been developed to perform many tasks until, with the march of time, it was generally replaced by internal combustion powered equipment.

Fortunately, numerous examples that were once laid aside, or allowed to become completely derelict, have been painstakingly restored by enthusiasts. Now returned to their former glory they provide a very fitting working reminder of this important part of our heritage.

Many companies built engines. These ranged considerably in size with the larger concerns operating in both the home and overseas markets. As a result British-built engines were to find themselves in many distant parts, some being especially designed for local conditions, eg straw burning.

Over the past few years quite a number that spent their entire working life abroad have returned home for preservation. Those which were in hot dry climates stood the passage of time best, although they were invariably stripped of brass and copperwork. Many were to return as derelict hulks, including among them designs long since disappeared from the British Isles.

What was thought of a few years ago as beyond restoration has in many cases — after a great many hours of painstaking work and considerable cost — been restored to full working order. Construction of new boiler barrels and fireboxes is now regularly undertaken. Even new castings for cylinder blocks have been produced — albeit at a price.

On the farm, the traction engine was used for many duties including haulage work and providing power to threshing machines, saw benches and other items of agricultural equipment. Ploughing was done by steam tractors pulling direct ploughs but more often by a pair of ploughing engines using equipment especially developed for this work. The Leeds-based company, John Fowler & Co (Leeds) Ltd, was to become a market leader, over the years introducing several designs with a very comprehensive range of equipment to use with steam power. Other companies, including Aveling & Porter, Burrell and McLaren, also built engines for this work.

On the roads undoubtedly the finest engines were the Showman's Road Locomotives with their polished brasswork, dynamos and, in the majority of cases, gleaming paintwork. These were responsible for hauling the fairground rides, which often comprised several heavily loaded wagons. Road conditions generally were certainly different from those of today, some of the routes taken having sharp bends and steep hills. It was not uncommon for a load to be split, the engine returning for the second portion. In the early days rough surfaces and potholes were among the hazards, with the engines on straked wheels presenting an unforgettable ride for the crew.

Once on the fairground some engines were used to assemble the rides, and these had jib cranes for handling heavy cars. When the fair was open the Showman's Road Locomotives provided the power for the rides and, in the majority of cases, lights. Here again, one company was to become very well known for this type of engine, this was

Charles Burrell & Sons Ltd of Thetford, Norfolk, a company which built fine examples over the years, of which many have survived. Other companies well-known for their 'Showmans' were Fowler's of Leeds, and Foster's of Lincoln, both building engines which were very highly thought of by the travelling showmen. Foden's, Garrett's of Leiston and Brown & May of Devizes were among other companies which also built this type of engine. Examples constructed by all of these are in preservation; the last three named companies are, however, represented by just one survivor in each case.

There was also a demand from showmen for a lighter, speedier, more easily handled engine for the smaller loads and these were to become known as 'Showman's Tractors'. Most, like their larger cousins, had a dynamo fitted on a bracket at the front, full canopy and, in most cases, lights.

Many heavy loads required moving around the country or locally. Powerful road locomotives were developed for this work with Fowler, Burrell and McLaren building many of the best-known surviving examples, although several other companies were also involved in this market. Road locomotives performed countless Herculean feats, hauling huge boilers, transformers and the like, often from one end of the country to the other. As can be imagined, the route taken needed careful planning to avoid weight restrictions, low bridges, difficult turns and many other hazards for these slow, long, extremely bulky loads.

Always sure to attract attention at any event which they attend are the road locomotives fitted with a crane. There are several very fine examples in preservation; these include two Fowler 'B6' class 'Super Lions', *Duke of York* and

Wolverhampton Wanderer, built in 1928 and 1929 respectively. Burrells to survive include *Old Tim* built in 1910. Despite this particular engine having a very hard working life, often 24hr a day, it has still retained its original livery, although doubtless the time will eventually come when it will need a complete repaint.

Lighter loads were handled by steam tractors, capable of being operated by one man. Many examples of this type were built for War Department service during World War 1. After hostilities ceased they were offered for sale. Indeed, quite a large number of those which we see today started their working life in government service.

Building and repairing the highways is an important task; up until the mid-1960s examples of the well-known steam rollers could still be found working. Many others had been laid aside in council and contractors' yards, replaced by diesel powered equipment. Around this time it was not uncommon for some of these to be advertised for sale; many changed hands for very reasonable figures. Traction engine rallies had been held for a number of years, as a result many rollers were saved for preservation.

Most engine builders regarded the construction of steam rollers as a very important market, not just for home but also overseas. Undoubtedly, the highest number in preservation are examples built by Aveling & Porter, although considerable numbers built by other companies survive, especially those constructed by Wallis & Steevens of Basingstoke.

Over the years, engines already in preservation have been sold to new owners overseas, with some going as far as Australia. Others have gone to new homes on the Continent and Scandinavia. This has been more than

offset by those which have returned.

Restoring a derelict engine is a long and costly undertaking; quite a considerable number while saved from the cutters torch have had little or nothing done to them for various reasons. Nevertheless, every season usually sees one or more making their rally début, attracting considerable attention from enginemen and enthusiasts alike. Among those which are likely to appear in the not-too-distant future are several Showman's Road Locomotives; some did attend very early rallies and have not been seen in public since.

In recent years, the general trend has departed from competitive events to displaying engines working on duties for which they were designed. Ploughing demonstrations now take place regularly; wood sawing, timber hauling, road making and repairing, threshing and stone breaking can also be seen. Undoubtedly, these working demonstrations attract considerable attention, although it is the heavy haulage displays that are the greatest crowd pullers. Given a hilly route and a large heavy load, you have a sure recipe to hear the engines working. Usually two or three are at the head of the largest with another at the rear.

The pictures in this volume have been very carefully chosen to provide a representative selection of engines in preservation over the years, at the same time including several rare and unusual examples. Keen observers will notice the absence of steam wagons; this is because they are a very important subject in their own right.

Eric Sawford
Huntingdon
February 1995

Above:
In 1920 two Fowler R3 class Showman's Road Locomotives were supplied to John Murphy, a Gateshead, Co Durham-based showman. The engine Nos 15652/3 were named *Repulse* and *Renown* respectively. These engines travelled for nearly 20 years with a 'Proud Peacock' ride. With the onset of World War 2 both were used on timber work under a Government contract. The engine in this picture is *Renown* which is now preserved in Derbyshire and is often seen in many parts of this country and on the Continent. After purchase by her present owners, 20 years ago, the Fowler was thoroughly overhauled to a high standard. Sister engine *Repulse* has also survived and is occasionally to be seen at events with its companion.

Left:
This Burrell 5nhp, No 3950, left the company works in 1924 as a road locomotive, spending its first years on general haulage work. It was normal practice for several of the engine builders to exhibit their latest designs at major agricultural shows, this Burrell being exhibited at the Royal Agricultural Society of England Annual Show.

In the early 1930s the engine passed into the ownership of Swindon-based showmen R. Edwards & Son, with whom it was converted to showman's specification and named *Progress*. It travelled with this owner for many years until, like so many of the once-proud Showman's Road Locomotives, it was replaced by diesel-powered equipment.

Above right:
The Busy Bee is an example of the 5nhp 'Devonshire Type' Showman's Road Locomotive built by Burrells in 1914. The engine spent much of its showland life in the northwest in the ownership of Taylor Bros, Workington, pulling their unique 'Alpine Motors Ride'. The final working years of this Burrell were spent, like so many others, on much more mundane agricultural work.

This engine has now been in preservation with the same owner for longer than it was in commercial service, having been rescued for preservation in 1952. It is interesting to note that, when its owner moved, the engine travelled the 250 miles to its new home under its own steam.

Right:
A very popular demonstration is when one of Frank Lythgoe's collection of Showman's Road Locomotives is used to tow six or seven engines of a similar type around the main ring. Despite the massive load behind this powerful Burrell No 3093 *Dreadnought*, it presented no problems. This engine was built in 1909 and spent its entire working life on the fairgrounds in the ownership of the Midland-based Holland family.

Left:

The Burrell 8nhp Special Scenic Road Locomotive *Dragon* is also widely known by the name *Pride of the Fens*. This engine was built in 1921 as Works No 3912 for the well-known Bristol-based showmen Anderton & Rowland. It operated throughout the West Country.

Dragon, which is renowned for its fine brasswork, has smaller diameter rear wheels; this is a great advantage on the hilly routes in the West Country.

Anderton & Rowland operated a fleet of Burrell Showman's Road Locomotives, three being 'Scenics' including *Dragon*. In all, five showman's engines once owned by this company have survived into preservation.

Above:

The Burrell 5nhp Showman's Road Locomotive *Nero* is preserved in Norfolk. On this occasion it was attending one of the popular engine events held at the Bressingham Steam Museum. *Nero* and sister engine *Rajah* toured the length and breadth of the country hauling Bostock & Wombwell's Travelling Menagerie, achieving the distinction of being the most widely travelled showman's engines. *Nero*, Works No 3669, is a 5nhp engine built in 1915.

Below:

This Burrell 7nhp Showman's Road Locomotive, No 3526 *Lightning II*, has the distinction of being the only showman's engine to leave the Thetford works painted green. The engine was supplied to the showmen, Emerson & Hazard, who were based in Whitehaven, Cumberland.

Lightning II is also well-known as the last engine to be used on heavy haulage work in Great Britain; this was as recently as 1957. In its green livery, this showman's engine stands out well when in company with other 'Burrells' with their more usual maroon paintwork.

This Burrell 10nhp Showmen's Special Scenic Road Locomotive *Dolphin*, built in 1925 as Works No 4030, was the last of a long line of showmen's locomotives constructed at the famous Thetford works.

Over the years the engine has had several showground owners and, as a result, several name changes. The Burrell's first owner was William Davis, based in Stoke-on-Trent, who named it *The Dolphin*. After being sold to John Shaw, Sheffield, it became *The Guv'nor* and finally to H. J. Wallis of Seaforth, Lancashire, who changed it yet again, this time to *The Commando*. In preservation it has reverted to its original showground name.

Right:
Brown & May of Devizes, Wiltshire, did not build many Showman's Road Locomotives. Only one survives: 6nhp No 8742 *General Buller* built in 1912, which was the last example constructed by the company.

This engine was built for J. Cooke, a showman based in North Wales travelling with a set of galloping horses. *General Buller* and the ride were later sold to Mellor Bros based in Nottingham. In the mid-1930s the Brown & May found itself on agricultural work, mainly threshing, in Lincolnshire. In 1970 the engine was restored to full showman's specification after standing derelict for many years. *General Buller* is still preserved in Lincolnshire and can be seen at events throughout the country.

Left:
This Burrell Showman's Road Locomotive, No 3979 *Earl Haig*, was completed in 1924 and supplied new to W. J. Taylor at Midsomer Norton. Ten years later it passed into the ownership of Gloucester-based showmen Symonds & Cook when it was converted to showman's specification, travelling with their 'Century Jungle Speedway' throughout the West Country with occasional visits to the London area.

In the early 1940s the Burrell was sold to Darbys of Sutton, well-known engine operators in Cambridgeshire and the surrounding district. When the engine was rescued for preservation in the early 1960s it had become derelict; after a long and extensive rebuild it was to appear several years ago on the rally fields in superb mechanical and external condition — as it was in its showland days.

Earl Haig has attended many events in East Anglia and Yorkshire, and also the well-known Great Dorset Steam Fair.

Below:

Wm Foster & Co Ltd of Lincoln was well-known for its Showman's Road Locomotives, which were very popular engines on the fairgrounds. Only seven examples built by this company have survived. The one we see here is 10nhp No 14632 *Success* which is the youngest of the seven, being completed in 1934.

The engine was supplied new to Hibble & Mellor, Nottingham-based showmen travelling extensively in the Midlands until the early 1940s. The Foster then passed into the hands of J. Hardwick of Ewell. Fortunately, *Success* survived to be purchased by Darbys of Sutton and eventually entered preservation. Since then it has been extensively overhauled. *Success* and *The Leader* are only two 10nhp examples of the seven survivors.

Left:

The Burrell 8nhp Showman's Road Locomotive No 2072 *The Masterpiece* is one of the oldest surviving showman's engines built by the company. It is also the oldest surviving double-crank compound of this type. Completed in 1898, *The Masterpiece* was supplied new to John Cole Amusements, Bristol, remaining with the same owners until sold for preservation. Over the years the engine found itself employed in other duties; during the war this included providing power to military establishments and tree pulling. *The Masterpiece* continued working until well into the 1940s when it was laid aside at the owner's Bristol base, the ravages of time gradually taking their toll.

   This engine still retains straked wheels in keeping with the Burrell's original specification. Extensive rebuilding was necessary during restoration which took several years to complete.

Right:

Fowler 'A5' class Showman's Road Locomotive No 11108 *Dreadnought* was built at Leeds in 1909. Being completed towards the end of the year, it was selected by the company for exhibition at the Smithfield Show, London, held in December. Most of the major engine building companies displayed examples of their latest construction at this show.

   Several Showman's Road Locomotives carry the name *Dreadnought*; this engine travelled with Coles' 'Venetian Gondolas'.

   Showman's Road Locomotives were called upon to haul considerable loads in their working days. This could often include hauling five or more trailers, which required a high degree of skill by the engine crew. Road surfaces in those days were considerably different: hilly routes, sharp bends and narrow gateways were just some of the problems

Left:
Many engine builders had a five-ton tractor in their range. Naturally, Burrell, with its wide experience in road engines, was also involoved with this market. Following the companies success in winning the RAC Gold Medal, its tractors were to become widely known as the 'Burrell Gold Medal Tractor'. Many of these very useful engines were to find their way into showland service, others spent their entire working lives on haulage work.

This engine, Work's No 3433 *Peter Pan*, was completed in 1912 and exhibited at the Smithfield Show the same year. It went to G. Kemp & Co Aldershot, Hants, for timber and brick haulage. The tractor was to spend 16 years on this type of work until it changed hands and was converted to a showman's tractor, being used as such by its new owners, Coles of Chichester. It was purchased for preservation in 1953.

Below left:
This Burrell tractor, No 3191, was one of a number ordered by the War Department following the successful use of steam tractors in the South African War. Burrell Works No 3191 was built in April 1910 and allocated to the Army Service Corps No 77. It was fitted with a forward-mounted jib crane with a lifting capacity of two tons, and larger belly tanks.

After World War 1 many engines were surplus to requirements and offered for sale. Following a short period in private ownership, No 3191 was purchased by G. A. Whittle of Woking, Surrey. Converted and named *Furious*, the engine assisted with this showman's set of gallopers and cakewalk. After a time it was part-exchanged for a Burrell Showman's Road Locomotive, but was later repurchased and fitted with generating equipment.

Right:
Garrett's of Leiston, Suffolk, built over 20 4CD tractors in 1913 including No 31193 *Henrietta*, which was completed in May of that year. This engine started its working life hauling stone, and remained on these duties until 1937 when it was sold to Montgomery Council. Five years later it changed hands again, going to Messrs Corfields Highway Contractors who converted it to a roller. It was eventually to be laid aside and, like so many once-proud engines, became derelict. When purchased for preservation it was restored as a showman's tractor.

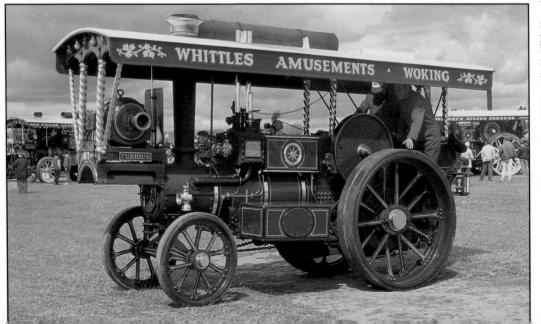

Left:
This Burrell 'Gold Medal' tractor, No 3453, was built in 1913 and supplied as a showman's tractor to W. Sedgwick, owner of a menagerie based in Oldham, Lancashire. Carrying the name *The May*, one of its principal duties was hauling the owner's 'American Jungle' ride.

In 1950 the Burrell was sold to John Downs. It then travelled with a set of gallopers. The engine is still with this showman and can be seen at events still occasionally working with the ride.

Over 30 'Gold Medal' tractors are in preservation, mostly in the United Kingdom, but there are also examples in The Netherlands and New Zealand.

Below left:
Garrett's built 514 of these very popular 4CD tractors, with a large number going to the War Department during World War 1, although this particular engine was not one of them.

Works No 32969 *Countess* was completed in February 1917 and used on general haulage duties — conversion to showman's specification was done during preservation. The engine has undergone a thorough overhaul in recent years and at some stage has been fitted with a superbly constructed mahogany canopy. This picture of *Countess* was taken at the 1992 Bressingham rally, the first to be held at this location for over 20 years.

Below:
This Burrell 'Gold Medal' tractor was another engine exhibited at the world-famous Smithfield Show. The tractor, No 3631 built in 1914, now carries the name *Kathleen*. After the show the Burrell was supplied to W. Gritt of Romsey, Hampshire, who was both a quarry owner and a showman. At that time, the engine carried the name *Pride of Romsey*. In 1933 it passed into the ownership of Maurice Stokes of Basingstoke, being converted to showman's specification. With its name changed to *Bluebird*, it was used to haul and provide power for a set of 'Chair o' Planes'.

Rescued for preservation in 1959 the engine was again renamed, this time *Kathleen*. The Burrell has undergone a major rebuild in recent years including a new boiler barrel and firebox.

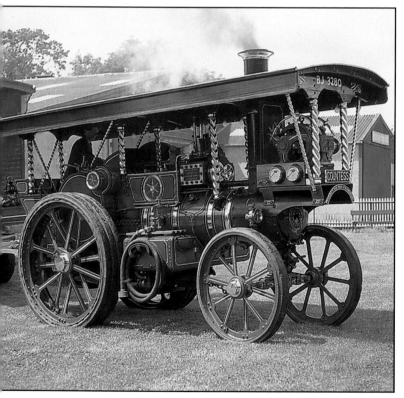

Left:

The Mighty Atom (Works No 33305 built in 1918) is one of the large batch of Garrett 4CD tractors built for the War Department during World War 1.

After hostilities had ceased, large quantities of equipment became surplus to requirements and were sold to private individuals. Many 4CD tractors were offered for sale including this one, which went to Harrison Bros of Bristol and was converted to a showman's tractor. It later passed into the ownership of Edwards Bros, Croydon-based showmen; the engine then worked with a set of gallopers.

During World War 2 the Garrett was used on agricultural duties, especially threshing work and, later, timber haulage. The engine was purchased for preservation just over 30 years ago.

Above:

The Garrett 4CD tractor was undoubtedly one of the most successful designs produced by this company based at Leiston, Suffolk.

This example, Works No 33091, was one of those supplied to the War Department, being completed in April 1918. After the war it was purchased by Fred Harris, a Sussex-based showman. At that time the engine carried the name *Valencia*, but this has since changed to *Margaret*.

Over the years a number of Garrett tractors were used by showmen. Some were of new construction going straight into showland service but the majority were engines that had been employed on other work before purchase by fairground equipment operators.

Left:

Wm Allchin Ltd of Globe Works, Northampton, built a sizeable number of engines and wagons. Works No 1415 is an example of the 7nhp single-cylinder design.

This engine was built in 1907, going new to Mr Turk, a Kent farmer, and remaining with the family for all of its working life.

It is now preserved on the Isle of Wight. The Allchin has become a regular entrant at the Great Dorset Steam Fair, travelling to the event under its own steam on several occasions. This picture of *The Havenstreet Queen* was taken while attending this event.

Above right:

This magnificent 'B5' class Fowler Crane Engine is Works No 8920, built at Leeds in 1901. It was supplied new to Stuart Dodds, Leith; three years later the company was purchased by John Wilkinson. For 23 years the engine was in regular use until it was decided that it was uneconomical. Fortunately the Fowler was provided with cover from the elements — in 1959 the engine was moved into the workshops where it was to remain for over 20 years. In 1988 it was sold for preservation; after three years the Fowler changed hands; this time a full overhaul was carried out. *The Great North* is now preserved in County Durham and has attended many events, some a considerable distance from its home base.

Right:

These three magnificently restored Burrell Road Locomotives made a fine sight standing in brilliant sunshine at Roxton Rally.

Nearest the camera is 6nhp No 3395 *The Dalesman,* built in 1912 for J. Hancock of Exeter, which was used on heavy haulage by this company until 1925 when it passed into the ownership of Hentons of Howpass. Next in line is *Lord Roberts,* Work's No 3057 built in 1908, which was supplied new to Wm Smith of North Warnborough. One of the engine's principal duties was hauling bricks. In 1919 it moved north to an owner in Binbrook, Lincolnshire.

The third Road Locomotive is No 3593 *Duke of Kent,* built in 1914 for C. Tassell of Chatham. After two other owners, it was purchased for preservation in 1973.

Below:
Burrell 5nhp No 3777 *Queen Mary* was completed at Thetford in
December 1917 as a Road Locomotive, going to an owner in Somerset
where it spent most of its working life on stone and brick haulage. The
engine was last used in 1948; afterwards, being laid aside like so many
once proud engines, it became derelict.

This Burrell is still fitted with belly tanks and is on straked wheels. The
flywheel is a spoked pattern.

Restoration took place over a number of years, the engine making its
appearance at events in East Anglia a few years ago.

Right:
Fowler Type TE2 7nhp haulage and winding engines were known as
'Russian Fowlers'. This was the result of a substantial order for engines of
this type being placed by the Russian military authorities. Further engines
were exported, whilst others were used by the British Army or purchased
by private customers when the contract was cancelled.

Works No 14933 *Challenger* was built at Leeds in 1917. This engine
spent most of its working life near Sleaford in Lincolnshire. In 1948 the
Fowler was purchased by Mr Crawford and was one of the first engines
restored for preservation just four years later.

The winding drum can be seen mounted underneath the boiler. This
picture was taken at Carrington Rally in 1992; the Fowler is usually only
to be seen at events held within the county of Lincolnshire.

Left:
Swirling, choking dust was a problem as the Amalgamated Heavy Haulage team arrive with its load at the Great Dorset Steam Fair. The railway locomotive on the trailer was from the Swanage Railway.

The lead engine is Fowler 8nhp No 17105 *Atlas*, built in 1928, which was supplied new to Norman E. Box Heavy Haulage Contractors. Next is 10nhp Fowler 'Super Lion' No 17106 *Duke of York* minus crane jib. Bringing up the rear, almost obscured by dust, is Burrell 8nhp Road Locomotive No 3057 *Lord Roberts*, which was built in 1908.

Below left:
Another well-known Burrell Road Locomotive is No 3829 *His Majesty*, which was built in 1920. The first owners of the 6nhp Compound were based at Liskeard, Cornwall. After a short time the engine passed into the ownership of J. Hickey & Son Ltd, when it was used for heavy haulage in the London area and then as a crane engine until 1950. After a considerable period of time a decision was made to rebuild and restore the 'crane engine' to its former glory. It made only a few rally appearances while still owned by the company in the very early 1960s.

His Majesty carried various embellishments acquired while being owned by this company — the brass ring and star on the chimney — although mostly appearing without the crane jib fitted at that time. It is now to be seen on the rally fields with the crane fully operational.

Right:
This Fowler 6nhp Class A4 Road Locomotive, No 8712 *Pride of Wales*, is among the oldest surviving road engines built by the company, being completed in July 1900.

The engine was supplied new to J. H. & R. O. Morse Haulage Contractors based at Narberth, Pembrokeshire, South Wales. Among its duties were stone haulage and, for a period of time, driving a stone crusher. After 40 years' service it was laid aside, gradually becoming derelict, spending another 40 years in this condition until purchased for preservation.

Pride of Wales is now to be seen at events in many parts of the country.

Above:
Swirling dust envelops Fowler Class A4 6nhp Compound Road Locomotive No 8712 *Pride of Wales* and McLaren 10nhp No 1652 *Boadicea* as they haul a large caterpillar tractor around the display area at the Great Dorset Steam Show. The two engines were built in Leeds, in 1900 and 1919 respectively.

Heavy haulage demonstrations have become a regular and very popular feature at this event.

Right:
This Fowler 7nhp Type TE2 Haulage and Winding engine is preserved in Holland. Built in 1917 as Works No 14925, *Windrush* was one of a large batch of this type built at this time, going to the Ministry of Munitions during World War 1, with duties including hauling and winching heavy guns. This picture was taken in 1993, the engine having just been completed following extensive restoration and appears at the Great Dorset Steam Fair. The winch and cable can be seen mounted underneath the boiler.

Above:
Fowler 'A5' class Compound three-speed Road Locomotive *City of Hull*, Works No 11111, was built in 1910. It went new to R. J. Hosdell & Co, Corn Merchants, Hull, where it remained for several years. After its service with Hosdell, the engine had several owners until rescued for preservation.

The Fowler is seen here with a four-wheeled articulated trailer which, like the engine, had received a complete overhaul.

Right:
This Burrell 8nhp Compound three-speed Road Locomotive, Works No 2789 *The President*, was built in 1905 as a Showman's Road Locomotive. It went new to President Kemp of Leicester as *Lord Kitchener* and was converted for heavy haulage before World War 1. It is now part of the famous Bressingham Collection, having been a static exhibit for many years.

The engine is still on straked wheels and carries additional brasswork, rings, stars, etc. While normally to be found inside the museum building, various engines are moved outside during the height of summer for the 'Photographers' Weekend'.

Above:
This Foden Road Locomotive, Works No 3534 *Monarch*, was built in 1913. Only five of this type of 'Colonial' engine were constructed; this was the only one to stay in this country, going new to the Earl of Derby's estate, where it was used on forestry work.

The engine has Foden's high-pressure system incorporating its patented double high valve. *Monarch* does not attend many events but can usually be seen at the Haddenham Rally near Ely, Cambridgeshire held in early September.

Above:
McLaren built 55 of the powerful 10nhp Road Locomotives for the War Office for hauling heavy guns. This engine, No 1652, was completed in January 1919 after the cessation of hostilities, so was never sent overseas. It was purchased privately and used on haulage work. Later it passed into the ownership of Filey-based showman Edward Corrigan, the McLaren returning to the works to emerge in showman's specification and named *Gigantic*. The engine was found to be too heavy for show work and was sold once again to Shaw & Gaskell of Hull, who used it for boiler haulage. Eventually the engine found itself on dredging work in East Anglia. The McLaren, now named *Boadicea*, is now a well-known and popular engine seen at many events, regularly giving heavy haulage displays.

33

Left:
Four engines, all built at Leeds by two well-known companies, await their turn to demonstrate their haulage capabilities.

Nearest the camera is a 10nhp Fowler 'Super Lion' No 17212 *Wolverhampton Wanderer*, built in 1929. Standing alongside is another Fowler, 10nhp 'B5' class *The Great North*, Works No 8920, built many years previously and leaving the works in April 1901. The other two engines are McLarens — the 6nhp General Purpose Engine No 757 *Loyalty*, built in 1904, spent most of its working life in Ireland, whilst last in the line-up is No 1421 *Captain Scott* built in 1913.

This picture was taken at the 1993 Great Dorset Steam Fair, one of the best events to see heavy haulage locomotives put through their paces.

Below left:
This picture of Fowler 7nhp Haulage & Winding engine Type TE2 was taken in the late 1960s when the Fowler was preserved at Holywell.

Works No 14950 was completed in January 1918 for the War Department to be used in the Russian War but was never sent. During preservation the Fowler was restored in its original War Department livery and attended a few local events. In October 1980 the Holywell collection was sold by auction with one exception, a Sentinel wagon.

The Fowler is still on straked wheels and has the haulage drum underneath the boiler. These engines were three-speed double crank compounds and generally regarded as a powerful towing engine.

Right:
Only three 10nhp McLaren Road Locomotives are preserved in the British Isles. One is the Showman's Road Locomotive No 1623 *Goliath*; the others are No 1652 *Boadicea* and this example, No 1332, now named *Gigantic*, built in 1912 which spent its working life in Australia before returning to Britain in the 1980s. For a period of time in preservation this engine ran in a maroon livery without a canopy and was named *Lionheart*.

McLaren built a sizeable number of 10nhp Road Locomotives for the War Department for use on haulage of heavy guns. The previously mentioned *Boadicea* was one of the batch but was never sent overseas.

Above:
This Aveling & Porter 6nhp three-speed Compound Road Locomotive, Works No 8471, was built in 1914 and is thought to be the only survivor of its type. The engine was supplied new to S. Frampton of Farnham, Surrey, and was used on general haulage, spending part of its working life in Cornwall.

By far the largest number of engines built by Aveling & Porter that have survived into preservation are steam rollers of various types and sizes.

There are also a number of general purpose traction engines and a few tractors. Only one of the wagons built by this company is in preservation in this country; this example returned from Australia several years ago. There are in addition three ploughing engines preserved, one of which was returned just two or three years ago. Another most interesting engine built by this company is the Type LC8 Road Locomotive constructed in 1901 for the Admiralty and used at HM Chatham Dockyard. It was later converted to a showman's specification for Charles Presland.

Right:
Very few engines built by J. & F. Howard, Britannia Iron Works, Bedford, have survived. This example, Works No 201, a 8nhp single-cylinder design, was built in 1872. The derelict remains were discovered at Dukes Aramac, Australia, with many of the essential parts missing. It is thought that it last worked in 1908 on a sheep-shearing plant.

The Howard returned home in 1982 and required very extensive rebuilding — new brasswork and flywheel were among the items needed. Despite this the engine was completely restored to a superb condition. The Howard was later to make a nostalgic return to its birthplace, where it was photographed outside Britannia Iron Works gateway.

Above:

Many traction engines built by Charles Burrell & Sons Ltd have survived into preservation. These include some early examples. Twenty-three of the survivors were built before the turn of the century, the oldest a 8nhp single-cylinder design dating back to 1877.

This engine is a 6nhp Compound, No 3125, built in 1909, which spent its early working years in Cornwall. It is seen here at the very popular Weeting Rally. Held not many miles from Thetford, the event usually has a number of Burrell traction engines present, including early examples.

Above:
This Marshall tractor, No 36258 *Punch*, was built in 1902 as a roller and went new to Gainsborough Council, thus working very close to its birthplace. The engine remained in the county of Lincolnshire until purchased in 1958 for preservation.

Marshall Sons & Co Ltd built up a large home and export market. Engines built by this company travelled far and wide throughout the world.

Fortunately several hundred Marshalls are in preservation, the vast majority being traction engines and rollers, with only a few tractors among them.

Left:
C. J. Fowell & Co Ltd of Cromwell Works, St Ives, in the county of Huntingdonshire as it was in those days, was not a large engine builder, construction being carried out somewhat erratically over the years. Seven examples built by this company have survived: six in Britain and one in Ireland.

This picture of three engines standing outside the old works entrance includes the oldest, Nos 91 and 92, built in 1902 and 1903 respectively with No 93 *The Abbot*, nearest the camera, built the following year. The site of the old works has long since been redeveloped. The engines built by Fowells are easily recognisable by the front wheels which are set fairly well back.

Below left:
Both of these Fowlers spent their working lives in Australia. Nearest the camera is a Class BAA, No 10773. Built in 1907 to a single-cylinder traction design, only nine examples of the type were built. This engine presents a very different appearance, not only because of its chimney but also its many other unusual features.

The other engine is a Class B5 8nhp Road Locomotive, No 9544 *Dalton Boy*, which was built in 1903. Both of these Fowlers returned home some considerable time ago in a derelict condition, requiring extensive rebuilding. They now present a fine sight at events mostly in the North of England.

Right:
For many years this splendid Ruston Proctor Class SH single-cylinder slide valve traction engine, No 35501 *The Muddler* (built in 1908), has attended rallies travelling under its own steam with a living-van on tow.

The engine was supplied new to Uriah Spratt of Thornston near Horncastle, Lincolnshire. The owner used the engine for road-haulage work for many years. In the early 1920s the engine changed hands, although it still remained in the county.

The Muddler is a regular entrant at many East Anglian events and is still to be found preserved in Lincolnshire.

Left:
Bright summer sunshine, a low camera angle and attractive background all combine to best effect in this picture of Burrell 7nhp traction engine No 2159, built in 1899.

The engine was attending a rally held at Bressingham. This very popular Norfolk event has been revived in recent years. Bressingham Steam Museum has a number of engines built by Burrells in its collection, among them Works No 3112, a 7nhp design built in 1909 which was the first arrival way back in 1961.

Right:
Other than the rally number on the side of this Burrell traction engine, which was being prepared for a working demonstration in Norfolk, this scene could just as easily have been taken during the engine's commercial life, although doubtless it would have presented a much more work-stained appearance in those days. Burrell No 4051 was built in 1926 and is a fine example of the 7nhp single-cylinder design.

Left:
The large road locomotives are always favourites at rallies wherever they are held in the country. Here we see Burrell 7nhp No 3257 *Clinker* leading three Fowlers into the main ring at Pickering, North Yorkshire. This example was built in 1911 and was supplied new to the Wingham Agricultural Implement Co. in Kent. It was used on road haulage for nine years before it moved to a new owner in Norfolk, spending the next few years on fen drainage work.

43

Above:
This Burrell 7nhp single-cylinder traction engine, No 4088 *Rosemarie*, has the distinction of being the last engine to be turned out from the Thetford works, the company collapsing in the Agricultural & General Engineers Combine. The last examples under the Burrell name were assembled by

Garrett's of Leiston, who had once been a rival company.

This engine was completed in September 1930. After a comparatively short working life it was laid aside, standing derelict for 18 years before it was purchased for preservation.

Above:
Gleaming in the bright sunshine of a spring day is Fowler 6nhp 'A4' class agricultural engine No 9230 built in 1902. It was supplied new to an owner in Gloucestershire and was used on various haulage and agricultural duties.

Fowlers produced both single-cylinder and compound designs of general purpose engines in considerable numbers up to World War 1, after which steam engines built by the company were mainly road rollers and the famous ploughing engines.

Far left:
Several of the major engine building companies were to be found at Lincoln or in the surrounding area. One of these was Ruston Proctor & Co Ltd, 'Sheaf Iron Works', Lincoln. This company was later to be succeeded by Ruston & Hornsby in 1919.

The engine in this picture was built by Ruston & Hornsby in 1920 and is a typical example of the company's 'SH' class. *Oliver* is Works No 113043, a 6nhp design traction engine which went new to Coxalls of Hinxton, Cambridgeshire. After four years it passed into the ownership of Mr Pumfrey, where it was to remain for over 50 years. Since changing hands again in the late 1970s *Oliver* has attended many events over a large area.

Left:
The city of Leeds was another important location for the construction of steam engines, both for the farms and highways and also for the railways. The largest of the agricultural and road-use engine builders was Fowler's. Another company in the area was The Mann Patent Steam Cart & Wagon Co Ltd, which was situated in the Hunslet district. Very few engines built by this company have survived and the majority of those that have are tractors.

The tractor in this picture was completed in October 1918 as Works No 1325 *Myfanwy*, going new to a farming co-operative on Anglesey and remaining there for its working life on threshing, haulage and wood sawing work.

Right:
The traction engine designs built by Marshall Sons & Co Ltd of Gainsborough, Lincolnshire, were very popular with farmers and agricultural contractors. The company built a large number both for the home market and overseas, many of which are still with us today.

This example of the company's 7nhp single-cylinder design is Works No 51025 *Margaret*, which was completed in December 1908. The engine spent its entire working life in Lincolnshire, mostly in the Spalding area.

Far right:
This fine example of the Garrett 4CD tractor spent part of its long and very varied working life on the fairgrounds. As a result it still carries some of the twisted brasswork. The engine was at that time owned by Henry Thurston and carried the name *Felix*. Originally built for the War Department, No 33295, now named *Princess Royal*, was offered for sale at the end of hostilities as were many other engines, wagons and countless other items of surplus equipment.

The Garrett 4CD tractor was a popular design, with over 500 being built over the years. Fortunately, a considerable number are still with us today.

Left:
Ruston & Hornsby was one of the engine builders to construct tractors for the War Department during World War 1. This engine, No 52453, was completed at Lincoln in 1918. After the war it was sold in the surplus equipment sales, its new owner using the engine for agricultural duties.

This is an example of the Class SCD 'Lincoln Imp' 5nhp design weighing five tons. Engines of this size were one of the types extensively used by the War Department and were supplied by several companies.

Right:
Engines which were intended for display at the prestigious Smithfield Show always received special attention. This Garrett 4CD tractor, No 34641, was completed in April 1925 and exhibited at the show that year. Production of these very popular engines was nearing its end. The last example was completed just three years later.

The engine was sold to Clare Rural District Council and is now part of the Bressingham collection, carrying the name *Bunty*. After a complete overhaul a few years ago it has been restored to its special show livery, chocolate brown and red, and is on display at Bressingham. It has attended a few local events.

Burrell 7nhp double-crank compound No 4049 *Daphne* was completed in August 1926, going new to C. & G. Bartrupt of Chelmsford, Essex, where it was to remain active for 20 years. The engine is seen here in charge of a loaded timber wagon at the Great Dorset Steam Fair.

Many traction engines of various types were used commercially on timber work. The Great Dorset has a wood sawing area where they can be seen at work driving various types of saw benches, loading timber and doing haulage work.

Left:
Two 7nhp Fowell traction engines stand in brilliant sunshine at Weeting. Fowell, based at St Ives in the county of Huntingdonshire (not to be confused with the popular Cornish holiday resort), was certainly not among the large engine builders. It did, however, construct a number of traction engines of 7nhp and 8nhp designs, most of which were sold locally. Seven of them still survive. On occasions three can be seen together at certain events. The two pictured here are (nearest the camera) the oldest survivor, No 91, built in 1902, and No 93 *The Abbot*, built in 1904.

Right:
Most of the Burrell traction engines which are seen at events today are not fitted with a canopy or belly tanks. But there are exceptions as can be seen on this magnificently restored Burrell 8nhp single-cylinder 'Keeling' Works No 3121, built in 1909.

Traction or general purpose engines were the most common type seen on farms. Very versatile, they were used for haulage, threshing tackle and providing power for items of equipment, including saw benches.

Right:
This massive Fowler 10nhp 'B6' class, No 17107, was built in 1928; the engine is seldom seen in public. In 1992 it made an appearance at the Carrington Park Rally — this popular event featuring Fowlers as its main attraction.

Built for stump pulling, the engine has a very heavy-duty winch and a 120yd steel rope of 1ft 25in diameter. This large Fowler weighs in at 20 tons and is 10ft 6in wide. It is the only engine of its type in Great Britain.

John Fowler & Co constructed a very wide range of steam engines and was particularly noted for its heavy haulage and ploughing designs. It also built steam wagons; one example still survives.

Far right:
This three-speed single-crank compound Burrell, No 3474 *Gay Girl*, was completed in May 1913 and was displayed new at the Highland Show. For most of its working life the engine was owned by Wallace Bros of Auchtermuchty, being used for road haulage and various agricultural work. Immediately below the nameplate are a set of 'spuds' — these were fitted to the rear wheels in heavy ground conditions.

Above:
This smart Fowler Road Locomotive, No 12902, 'Activity' Class D2 Compound 5nhp engine, was built at Leeds in September 1913. This engine has been used on a number of duties during its working life. When new it was purchased by a Kent market gardener who used it for transporting fruit to Covent Garden. On changing ownership, it was operated on general haulage and timber work in Gloucestershire and Worcestershire. Among its last work was threshing.

The engine is seen here with a typical Fowler traction wagon.

Right:
This Robey, No 29330, a three-speed compound engine, was built in 1910, going new to the Gibbons family. It performed a number of duties including threshing and stone-crushing, spending its entire life with the family. The engine, now in retirement, has attended a great many events over the years — note the large number of rally plaques carried.

Robey & Co Ltd was another of the builders to be found at Lincoln, constructing several different types at its Globe Works. Portables were still built by this company well into the 1940s.

Right:
The oldest Burrell traction engine thought to have survived is No 748, *Century*. Built in 1877 to an 8nhp single-cylinder design, it is preserved only a few miles from the famous Burrell works at Thetford.

As with so many engines, this Burrell was to become derelict, standing for over 30 years before being rescued. In the 1940s and 1950s one could often see agricultural engines in a derelict condition in farmyards — probably in the place where their fires had been dropped for the last time. Many were to end their days under the cutter's torch — at that time any engine requiring new boiler barrel or firebox work was rejected as being thought to be past economical restoration.

The Fowler 'BB1' class ploughing engines were very popular, with large numbers being built. As a result we are fortunate that a considerable number have in turn survived into preservation. These massive 16nhp engines weigh 20 tons. This example was built in 1919 as Works No 15336. For many years it carried the name *Janet*, but this has now changed to *Yorkshire Lad*.

When new this engine was supplied to Dennis Bros of Kirby, Lincolnshire. For many years this Fowler has travelled to events under its own steam, usually towing a living-van.

Burrell of Thetford is a name not usually associated with ploughing engines. But this 8nhp single-cylinder engine, No 777, and sister engine, No 776, both built in 1879, have been carefully restored in recent years and can now be seen in action at various events. The unique pair are owned by the Museum of East Anglian Life, Stowmarket.

The Burrells' first owner was at Woolavington. They were only there for a short time before going to an owner in Colchester, having been returned to Burrell's works in the meantime. After this they had several owners before being sold for scrap in 1935 to R. Edwards of Swindon, where they were to remain for 31 years. They were then purchased by the late Tom Paisley who commenced restoration of No 777. Both engines were sold at the auction in October 1980 to the late Tom Varley and subsequently sold to the Museum of East Anglian Life in 1984, one in working order, the other still in parts.

Above:
This superbly restored Fowler 16nhp 'BB1' ploughing engine (Works No 15345) was built in 1919. On occasions the opportunity is taken to use this Fowler and sister engine *Tweedledum* (Works No 15344) to perform ploughing work on the owner's farm. *Tweedledee* is seen here awaiting the whistle signal to commence the next pull. The 'BB1' design was very popular and fortunately a considerable number have survived into preservation.

Above:
This Howard ploughing engine built in 1876 is believed to be the only surviving example. It is an 8nhp single-cylinder design, the work's number having been lost in the mists of time as has much of its early history.

In 1916 the engine was owned by Baldwin Bros of Wadhurst, Sussex, and in 1929 it was sold to the Henry Ford Museum in the United States where it was to remain until 1991 when it was returned to this country and was exhibited at a number of events. After full restoration this engine is certain to attract much attention.

This unique Howard has a pair of rear-mounted cable drums. When photographed it was at the Banbury Rally.

61

Above:
This Fowler ploughing engine, No 13881, is one of the few remaining examples of the 16nhp 'AA6' class. Built in 1917, the engine was supplied new to Lord Rayleigh's estate in Essex.

Fowler's of Leeds also built several types of equipment for their use with these ploughing engines over a very long period of time. Fowlers that have survived into preservation range from the oldest, built in 1870, to the youngest, completed in 1929. Fortunately examples of many classes built over the years have survived — but not all; in some cases there is just a single example of a particular class.

Above:

Two Fowlers of different classes are made ready for the days events. Nearest the camera is 16nhp 'BB1' class No 15344 *Tweedledum*, which was built in 1919. Standing alongside is the more powerful and heavier 'AA' class 18nhp No 16053 *John*, built in 1925. Only six ploughing engines completed after this example was built have survived, the youngest pair being 'K7s' built in 1929. This 'AA' class Fowler and *Michael*, the other one of the pair, were supplied new to H. Carter of Tydd, near Holbeach, Lincolnshire. They remained there for 20 years before going to a new owner in the same county. This pair of ploughing engines have now been owned by the Museum of Lincolnshire Life since 1978.

Left:
This fine Fowler 8nhp single-cylinder ploughing engine was built in 1877 as Works No 3195 and is one of the most remarkable restoration projects in recent years. This engine and No 2861, built in the previous year, stood at Inkberrow from 1935 until being rescued a few years ago. By the time of their rescue both engines had become derelict after standing in the open for so long. No 3195 was the first to appear on the rally fields and has since been joined by the other veteran rescued at the same time.

Right:
This picture could just as easily have been taken during the engine's commercial life as there is nothing to betray that it was taken in preservation days except perhaps the overall cleanliness. Ploughing engines, in the majority of cases, received little in the way of cleaning from their owners.

Built in 1925 as Works No 15453, the engine was supplied to A. C. Cole together with the other one of the pair, No 15454. These engines carry the names *Saucy Sue* and *Bonzor Tom* respectively.

The engine is seen here ready for a cultivating demonstration on sandy Breckland loam at Weeting.

Above:
Heavy ground conditions show clearly on the wheels of this Fowler 'T1' class 12nhp ploughing engine, Works No 14253, which was built in 1916. The 'T1s' were double-drum engines. Spending most of its early years in Oxfordshire, this Fowler was later owned by Bomford & Evershed, where it completed its working days. This picture was taken at the Great Dorset Steam Fair, where several ploughing engines can usually be seen in operation working with various items of equipment.

Above:
Undoubtedly the largest type of Fowler ploughing engines to be seen at events is the 'Z7' class, a massive 22nhp design weighing 25 tons and fitted with two-speed drum. This example is Works No 15673, built in 1922. It spent its working life on the Sena sugar estates in Mozambique. Several of these huge engines have returned to this country in recent years, the dry African climate helping to preserve them. The width and tall chimneys of this particular class are especially noticeable when standing nearby.

Above:
McLarens of Leeds also built ploughing engines; two examples of these have survived into preservation in the British Isles. This engine is No BD 5504 *Hero*, a 16nhp design built in 1918. Now preserved in Cornwall, it has attended many events in various parts of the country in the 30-plus years since restoration. The other McLaren is a 12nhp engine, which is also a double-crank compound built in 1918 and preserved in Hampshire.

Above:

Ruston Proctor's 11-ton roller No 50735 was completed at Lincoln in May 1915. It is an example of the 'SCR' class — a compound design with slide vales. The roller did not have far to go to its first owner, which was Louth Borough Council, remaining with them for 20 years. The roller was then owned by several private highway contractors until it entered preservation in the early 1960s.

The company, Ruston Proctor & Co Ltd, was succeeded by Ruston & Hornsby Ltd in 1919. Five rollers built by the original company are in preservation.

Right:

Marshalls of Gainsborough, Lincolnshire, constructed a great many steam rollers for the home and overseas markets. This is a fine example of the 10-ton 'S' type: No 79087 built in 1925 — a single-cylinder engine fitted with piston valves. When new the roller was exhibited at the Peterborough Show and was purchased by Market Harborough Rural District Council, working until 1960 when it was purchased for preservation. The roller is now restored to its original livery, on display at the Peterborough Show.

Left:
Most of the larger engine building companies were involved in producing steam rollers. This example is a Fowler 'DH' class Compound 12-ton roller, Works No 16008, which was built in 1923. It spent its working life in County Durham, where it still is to be found in preservation.

Steam rollers were still in use during the 1960s, although most had been replaced by diesel counterparts. Often, although not in regular use, they were still capable of work. As the decade progressed many of these were offered for sale.

Below left:
Many Aveling & Porter steam rollers are in preservation; this one is, however, the only surviving example of the nine vertical twin-cylinder Shay-geared rollers built by the company. This engine is Works No 7411 of 1912. The tandem design operates with the twin-cylinder engine geared directly to the rear roll as can be seen in this picture.

Right:
Another splendid Fowler steam roller is this 12-ton Compound 'D5' class, Works No 15902, which was built in 1923. The engine was delivered new to Ashford Borough Council, Kent, where it remained for its entire working life until purchased for preservation in 1960. Most of the larger Borough and Rural District Councils owned their own steam rollers. Others used highway contractors for work in their area; many contractors operated steam rollers until they were replaced by modern diesel-powered counterparts.

Above:

This is an example of the 10-ton single-cylinder Aveling & Porter roller design — Works No 9283, built in 1920. Rollers of this type in various weights were a regular sight on our highways for a great many years, often travelling to and from locations under their own steam, usually towing a living-van. When not in use they were to be seen, often sheeted, in laybys, sometimes for considerable periods.

Above:

Wallis & Steevens of Basingstoke became well-known for its steam rollers over the years. In the early 1920s this far-sighted company introduced its outstanding 'Advance' design. This had two high-pressure cylinders and no flywheel, principally to avoid the risk of a depression on new road surfaces. The steering was a bevel through the rolls, eliminating the slack that occurred with chain-operated steering. Large numbers of these engines were built over a considerable period of time and quite a number have survived. This example is Works No 8096, built in 1935.

Left:
The Mann Patent Steam Cart & Wagon Co Ltd introduced a design under the name 'Mann Steam Cart'. For one-man operation and principally for direct ploughing, it could also be used with the cart body.

Works No 1425 *Little Jim* was built in 1920 and is seen here with a small 'riding' plough ready for a demonstration near Peterborough. Firing was done at the side of the firebox; this picture shows the small footplate and engine controls.

Right:
This rather unusual engine was introduced by Garrett's and known as the 'Suffolk Punch'. It was principally intended to counter the steadily increasing numbers of internal combustion-engined tractors. The design was well thought out but unfortunately did not prove popular and very few were built. Only this example, No 33180 *The Joker*, survives. Built in 1919, this 4nhp design is now to be found at the Garrett Museum, Leiston.

Over the years this unique engine has attended many events, covering a wide area.

Above:
Portable engines were constructed by many well-known engine builders over a very long period. They were designed to be towed to the work-site by horses and to be used to power many items of agricultural machinery: threshing drums, saw benches etc, either in the open or under barns. This engine was built by Marshall's of Gainsborough and is fitted with a round firebox.

Above:
This very rare portable engine was built by Young's of Diss, Norfolk, in 1910. It is an 8nhp single-cylinder design weighing five tons. This engine is the only survivor of the 14 built. It is normally under cover in the museum at Bressingham but usually several of the exhibits are moved outside annually for a special photographers' weekend. This was the occasion when this picture was taken in the splendid setting of Bressingham.

Left:
Another rare portable engine and also part of the Bressingham collection is the magnificent Burrell portable engine, Works No 2363. It was built at nearby Thetford in 1901, being a 10nhp compound design, and is thought to be the only example of its type in existence.

This engine spent its commercial life working on an estate, where it would have performed many different duties, and, in later years, at a pottery in the county of Suffolk.

Portable engines were built by Robey & Co Ltd until well into the 1940s.

Right:
Burrell of Thetford built many fine engines for agricultural use. These included both single and compound designs with several different power outputs. Fortunately, a considerable number have survived into preservation. No 3126, built in 1909, is a splendid example of the 6nhp compound traction engine, which was ideal for many applications.

The 'Heyday' series from IAN ALLAN Publishing